Teresa Mc Andle.

Specimen Sight-Reading Tests for Violin

GW00671203

Grades 6-8

The Associated Board of the Royal Schools of Music

3.75

GRADE 6

AB 2658

GRADE 6

GRADE 7

AB 2658

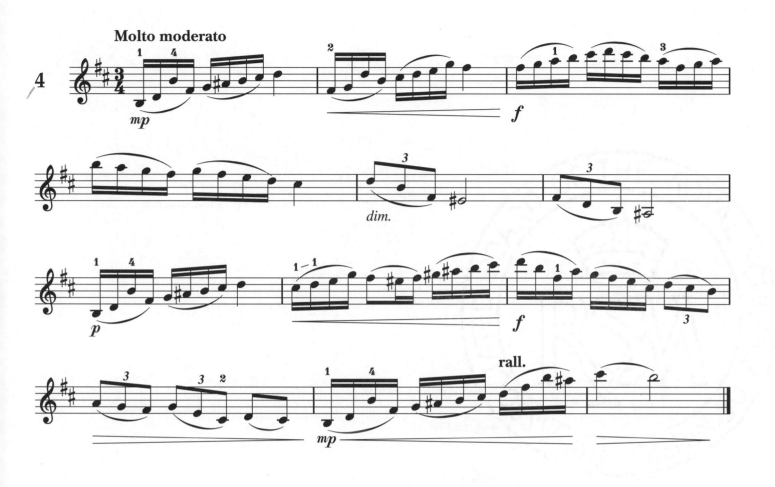

AB 2658

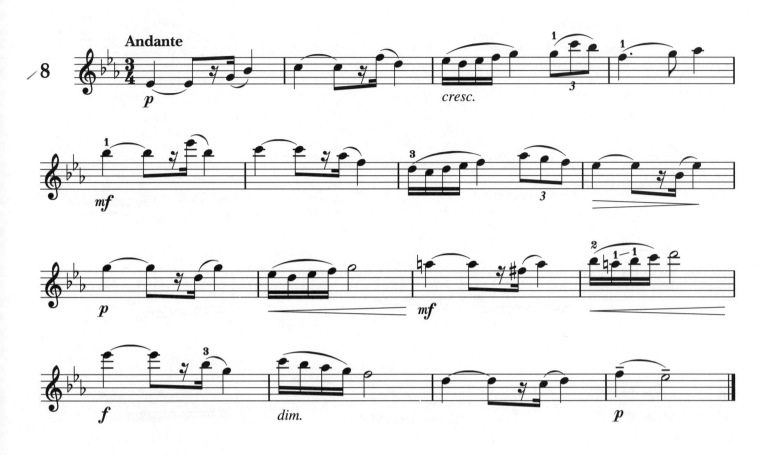

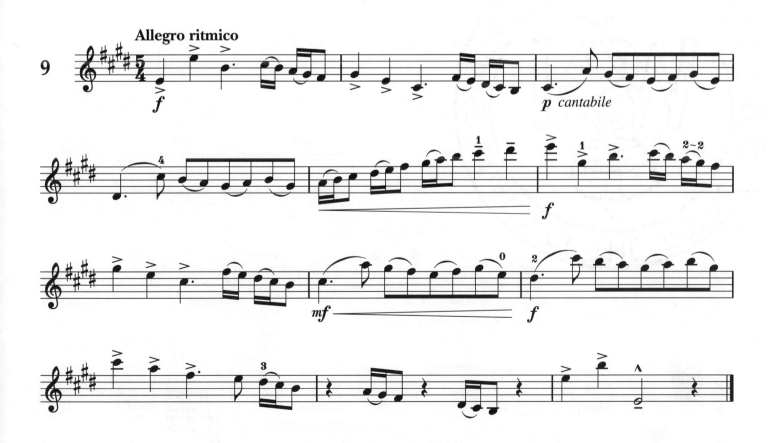

GRADE 7

AB 2658

12

Allegro agitato

13

Lento e dolce

AB 2658

GRADE 8

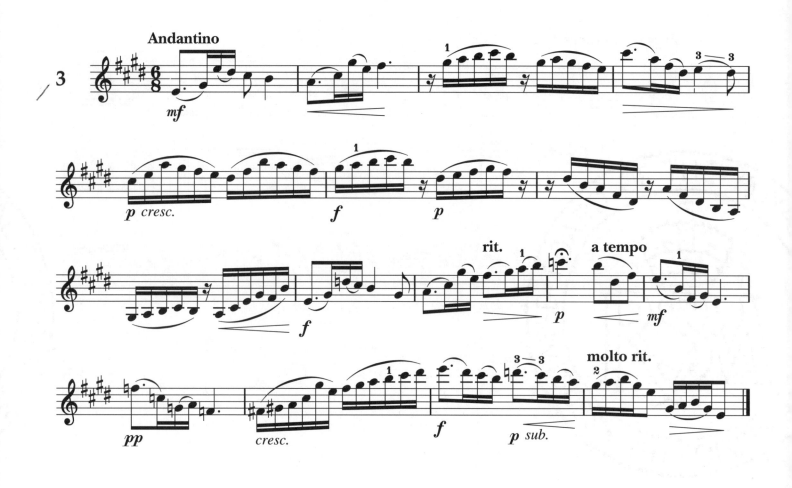

GRADE 8

7

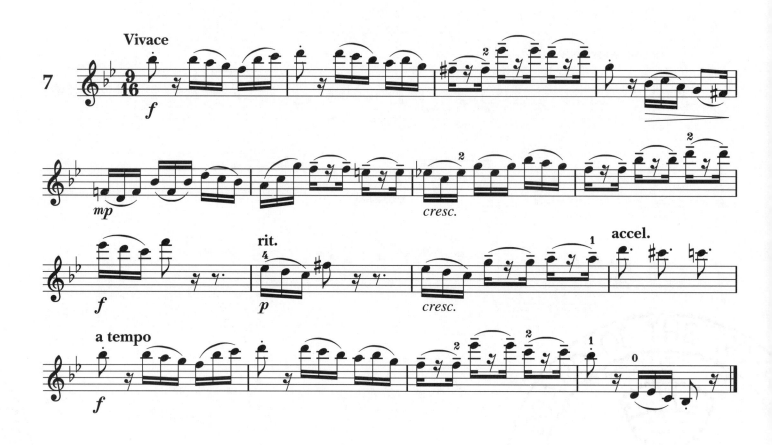

8

AB 2658

9

10

GRADE 8

17

Molto giocoso

18

Maestoso ma con moto